About the Book

This book ranges from sundials and Stonehenge to the radio-carbon dating of prehistoric measurement of a nanosecond (a thousand-millionth of a second). It explains some of the fascinating and still-evolving techniques of time measurement used by scientists.

All science advances in tiny steps, the result of painstaking observation and measurement. The *Yardsticks* books take some of the principal properties of matter which the scientist — whether chemist or engineer, materials scientist or plant pathologist — wants to measure. These properties are common to all sciences, so the authors draw their examples without reference to the classical divisions into "pure" and "applied" science. Each book extends across the widest range of its chosen property — in this book, time.

YARDSTICKS OF SCIENCE

Timothy Johnson

River of time

Illustrated with photographs and drawings

Coward-McCann, Inc.　　　　　**New York**

1475048

Contents

PHOTOGRAPHS

FIGURES

Preface

by David Fishlock

Science, once neatly split into the four great divisions of physics, chemistry, biology and mathematics, has become more and more fragmented. Today a bewildering 3,000-odd subspecies are distinguished — from astronomy and aerodynamics to wave mechanics and zoology.

A great deal of science is pursued for its own sake; with the aim, the romantic would have it, of pushing out the boundaries of knowledge. (Although one eminent modern scientist at least prefers to think of scientists "creeping along the boundaries with a magnifying glass.") Sometimes, as in the conquest of the Moon or the unraveling of the life processes, many different disciplines are harnessed to a common purpose. But whether practiced for its own sake or as part of some grand design, all science advances in tiny steps, the result of painstaking observation and measurement by the scientist.

You are all familiar with some of these measurements — you use them every day, whenever you tell the time, check the temperature, glance at the speedometer. An American scientist has estimated recently that, by adding to all these casual measurements (perhaps up to fifty a day for every one of us) all those made in industry and by scientists, we arrive at a total of 20 billion measurements made *every day* in the U.S.A. alone.

The *Yardsticks of Science* introduce you to some of the principal properties of matter which the scientist — whether

chemist or engineer, materials scientist or plant pathologist—
wants to measure. These properties are common to all science, so Mr. Johnson has drawn his examples without regard
to the modern, highly artificial division into "pure" and "applied" science. This book extends across the entire spectrum
of its chosen property, time.

1 How long ago?

The oldest things

What are the oldest things of all? People, animals and plants — in fact all living things — are quite young, of course. Even the giant redwood trees of California are new compared with the hills and mountains, although some of these trees are 3,000 years old.

The mountains themselves have been building up and wearing down throughout most of the Earth's history, so some of them are much older than others. As a rule the highest and most rugged mountains are also the newest because they have not had so much time to get worn away. The Alps and the Himalayas, including Everest, are only about 10 or 20 million years old, and many scientists believe they are still growing. I say "only," because these two huge ranges are young compared with the mountains of Scotland, which are 400 million years old, or the Appalachians in the United States, which were first thrown up 250 million years ago. Both these ranges were once much higher than they are now.

Before there can be mountains, there must be rocks to make them. New rocks are continually being formed from the lava spewed out in volcanic eruptions (volcanic rocks) and the sediments washed down by rivers and deposited on the seabed (sedimentary rocks). The oldest rocks are all volcanic, and the very oldest discovered so far, a granite from near Bulawayo in Southern Rhodesia, has an age estimated at 3.3 billion years. Scientists now believe that a crust began to form on the molten Earth as it cooled about 3.5 billion years ago, so there cannot be many rocks older than the Bulawayo granite.

But the Earth itself must be older. According to modern ideas the Sun, the Earth and the other planets — in fact, all of what we call the solar system — were formed at the same time from a huge cloud of material floating in space, rather like droplets of water condensing from a cloud of steam. This probably happened about 4.6 billion years ago. So much heat was involved in the process that the Earth had to cool for a billion years before a crust of solid rock could form on its surface.

Scientists can go even further back and make a guess at the age of the atoms in this original cloud of material. All substances are made up of atoms, which belong to any one of 92 different kinds, called elements. The simplest element is hydrogen, and all the atoms of the more complicated elements may have been built up from hydrogen atoms, perhaps under tremendous pressure and at very high temperatures in the middle of giant stars.

Although scientists cannot agree about the way it happened, or how hydrogen came to be there in the first place, they are able to say that some elements were still being formed as recently as 4.9 billion years ago — not long before the Earth itself, if you can get used to thinking in terms of billions of years. On the other hand some atoms of some elements are probably very much older than this — 8 or even 10 billion years old. Of all the things on the Earth these atoms must be the oldest, although there are probably stars and planets in some parts of the universe which are older still.

It is worth stopping to consider what a tremendous length of time is involved in these numbers. The Earth, 4.6 billion years old, is more than a million times as old as the oldest trees, which themselves started growing long before the birth of Christ. If you represented all the time that has passed since the beginning of the Earth by a line a mile long, that portion representing the 2,000 years since the birth of Christ would be shorter than the distance across a pinhead.

We cannot really get a mental picture of such huge lengths of time, although we can get used to talking about them. The important thing is to realize that the time that has passed since human history began is only a tiny part of the total age of the Earth. In the first part of this book I shall talk about the ways in which scientists have been able to reach back and measure these tremendous lengths of time; how they have put dates to things which happened in prehistoric times — often long before human beings ever appeared on the Earth. Many of these dates are still only roughly correct, but they are much more exact than was ever thought possible a hundred years ago, and no doubt they will be made more precise in future.

Asking the atoms

Perhaps you are wondering how it is possible to say when atoms and elements came into being, since even the Earth itself did not exist at the time. Scientists have been able to do it by asking the only things that were present at the occasion — the atoms themselves. In fact there are many ways in which atoms can be used as a kind of clock built into the Earth.

Probably you have heard of *radioactivity,* which is the result of atoms breaking up and giving off radiations — atomic fragments. Only a few atoms are radioactive, and these are said to belong to *radioisotopes.* All the other nonradioactive atoms are said to be in stable isotopes.

Isotope is the name given to a class of atoms which are all alike. Most of the 92 elements I mentioned earlier include several different isotopes, which are identified by the name of the element they belong to and a number.

For example, the radioisotopes we shall be talking about a lot are uranium-235 and uranium-238. The name shows that they both belong to the element uranium, so they are found together and are similar in most ways. The number tells us that one atom of uranium-235 is 235 times as heavy as the hydrogen atom, the simplest one of all, while atoms of uranium-238 are 238 times as heavy as hydrogen. This small difference in weight is enough to make an important difference between the two isotopes in their radioactivity.

Now imagine we have a piece of material with a thousand atoms of a radioisotope in it (Fig. 1). Every now and then one of the radioactive atoms "decays," which means it gives out a burst of radiation and changes into a different kind of atom — another isotope, in fact. This might be an isotope of the same, or a different, element. Nobody can say which one of the thousand atoms is going to do this next. But we do know that after a certain time there will be only 500 atoms — just half of the original radioisotope — left. The other 500 will all have decayed to something different.

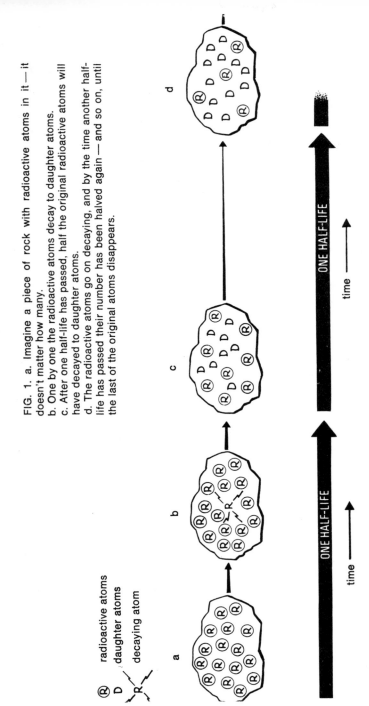

FIG. 1. a. Imagine a piece of rock with radioactive atoms in it — it doesn't matter how many.
b. One by one the radioactive atoms decay to daughter atoms.
c. After one half-life has passed, half the original radioactive atoms will have decayed to daughter atoms.
d. The radioactive atoms go on decaying, and by the time another half-life has passed their number has been halved again — and so on, until the last of the original atoms disappears.

Ⓡ radioactive atoms
D daughter atoms
Ⓡ̷ decaying atom

a   b   c   d

ONE HALF-LIFE   ONE HALF-LIFE

time   time

Nor does it matter how many atoms we started with. After a certain time half of them will have decayed; and this length of time is the same however many atoms there were at the beginning. The length of time it takes for half the atoms of a particular radioisotope to decay is called the *half-life* of the isotope. It is important to remember what the half-life is, because it is used as a kind of yardstick for lengths of time.

The other thing to remember is that a radioactive atom does not just disappear when it decays. It turns into a different kind of atom, often called the "daughter" isotope. In many cases it also sends out what is known as an *alpha particle,* which is an atom of helium.

Helium is a gas and, next to hydrogen, the simplest of all elements. As a radioisotope decays, the daughter isotope accumulates, and helium may accumulate too. The vital thing is that this happens at a steady, constant rate. The time it takes is not affected by the surroundings in any way at all. The radioisotope can be at the top of a mountain or in the deepest part of the ocean, in a refrigerator or a furnace — it will still decay at the same rate. So this provides us with an exact measure of very long periods of time. Let us see now how scientists use radioisotopes to "tell the time."

Before the Earth began

The fact that radioactive atoms still exist tells us roughly how old the elements must be. Radioactive and stable (non-radioactive) isotopes were created together when the elements were first formed, but the radioisotopes mostly decayed quite quickly to stable ones. All those which still survive in any quantity must have half-lives of hundreds of millions or billions of years.

One of the shorter-lived radioactive atoms still in existence is uranium-235, which has a half-life of 710 million years. If we remember that the half-life is the period it takes for *half* the atoms to decay, this tells us that the elements cannot have been formed more than about 10 billion years ago; or else, since the number of atoms of uranium-235 is halved every 710 million years, there would be very little of it left by now. On the other hand, uranium-236 has already disappeared from the Earth. Uranium-236 has a half-life of 24 million years, so it must have taken at least one billion years to decay so completely.

Now we know that the elements must be between one and 10 billion years old. By guessing that, to start with, there were probably about as many atoms of uranium-235 as of uranium-238, we can narrow the figures down a bit further. By now, because uranium-235 decays more than six times as

FIG. 2. When the elements were first formed there was probably as much uranium-235 as uranium-238. But because uranium-235 decays to lead-207 six times as fast as uranium-238 decays to lead-208, there are now 137 atoms of uranium-238 for every one of uranium-235.

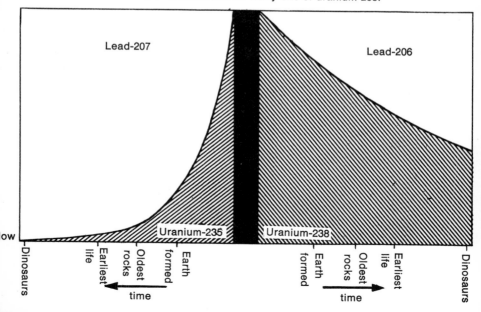

quickly as uranium-238, there is only one atom of uranium-235 for each 137 atoms of uranium-238. Working backward from this fact, scientists can calculate that about 6 billion years ago there were the same amounts of each isotope (Fig. 2).

Six billion years is probably just an average age for the elements, not an exact one. According to the latest ideas the process of "cooking" hydrogen in giant stars to build up the heavier, more complicated elements must have taken several billion years. There are clues that it went on almost up to the time when the solar system began to form, but of this we are not yet so certain.

Old Testament to meteorites

In the seventeenth century James Ussher, Archbishop of Ulster in the north of Ireland, confidently declared that the Earth was created at nine o'clock on the morning of October 12 in the year 4004 B.C. He arrived at this date after a scholarly study of the Old Testament, and, although it seems absurd now, his conclusion was generally believed for a long time.

Only in the nineteenth century did geologists (men who study the Earth's rocks) begin to realize that our world must be millions of years old. This soon led to a great argument between the physicists (who study the behavior of all kinds of matter) and the geologists. The physicists, led by an Englishman, Lord Kelvin, said the Earth could not be more than 20 to 40 million years old because it still has a hot interior, which would have cooled down in a longer period. The geologists believed it must be 10 or 20 times older because of the time needed to lay down all the sedimentary rocks.

Then radioactivity was discovered, and people began to realize that some of the heat inside the Earth came from radioactive atoms as they decayed. In 1907 Bertram Boltwood, an American chemist working in England, suggested that radioactivity might be used to measure the ages of rocks.

Boltwood was working at Cambridge University with Lord Rutherford, the man who first worked out the structure of the atom. Rutherford's group had already shown that uranium-235, uranium-238 and thorium-232, another radioisotope found in rocks, all decay to isotopes of the metal lead, giving off helium gas in the process.

Boltwood's idea was to measure the amount of the different lead isotopes and of helium in a rock, and also the amount of thorium that remained. The half-lives of the uranium and thorium isotopes were already known, so it would be fairly straightforward to work out how long it had taken for the lead and helium to accumulate.

This information would tell us how old the rock was, from the time when it first solidified and began collecting lead and helium from radioactive decay, after pouring as lava from a volcano in an eruption long ago. (It is almost always volcanic rocks which include large amounts of uranium or thorium, so they can be dated in this way.)

When scientists tried out Boltwood's suggestion, they soon proved that the Earth must be even older than the geologists thought. By 1950, when many rocks had been dated by radioactivity, the Earth was thought to have an age of about 3 billion years. But now scientists believe it is 4.6 billion years old, give or take a few hundred million. Although they cannot be quite as exact as Archbishop Ussher, they feel fairly confident that this is the right answer at last.

One complication with radioactive dating is the need to allow for any lead that was in the lava to start with. Fortunately there are four different isotopes of lead. Three of them, lead-206, lead-207 and lead-208, are daughter isotopes of uranium and thorium; but the other one, lead-204, is an orphan, so to speak. If there is any lead-204 in a rock scientists know it must have been there since the rock was formed, because it is not created by radioactive decay. They can use the amount of lead-204 as a clue to the amount of the other lead isotopes that were in the rock to start with, and allow for them in calculating its age.

Scientists soon realized they could use just the same method to measure the age of the Earth, if only they knew how much lead there was in it originally. Our world still has the same amount of lead-204 in it as it started with, but the quantity of the other lead isotopes has been steadily increasing because of radioactivity.

In new rocks there are usually about 18 atoms of lead-206 to every one of lead-204. On the other hand, in some of the oldest rocks, such as that from the Rosetta Mine in South Africa, there are less than 13 atoms of lead-206 to each one of lead-204. Scientists can work out fairly easily from this how old the Rosetta Mine lead must be. The answer comes to about 3.1 billion years.

Had they found a sample of the Earth's original lead, they could easily have done the same sum to find the age of the Earth. But for a long time there seemed to be no hope of finding any original lead, so the geologists had more or less to guess the Earth's age from the age of its rocks and other indirect clues.

Then about 1947 Dr. Harrison Brown, an American atomic

FIG. 3. Meteorites were formed at the same time as the Earth from a cloud of gas and dust around the Sun. But they cooled and solidified much more quickly than the Earth, so the original lead in them was kept pure. Now, when they fall to Earth, scientists can analyze them to find out what original lead was like.

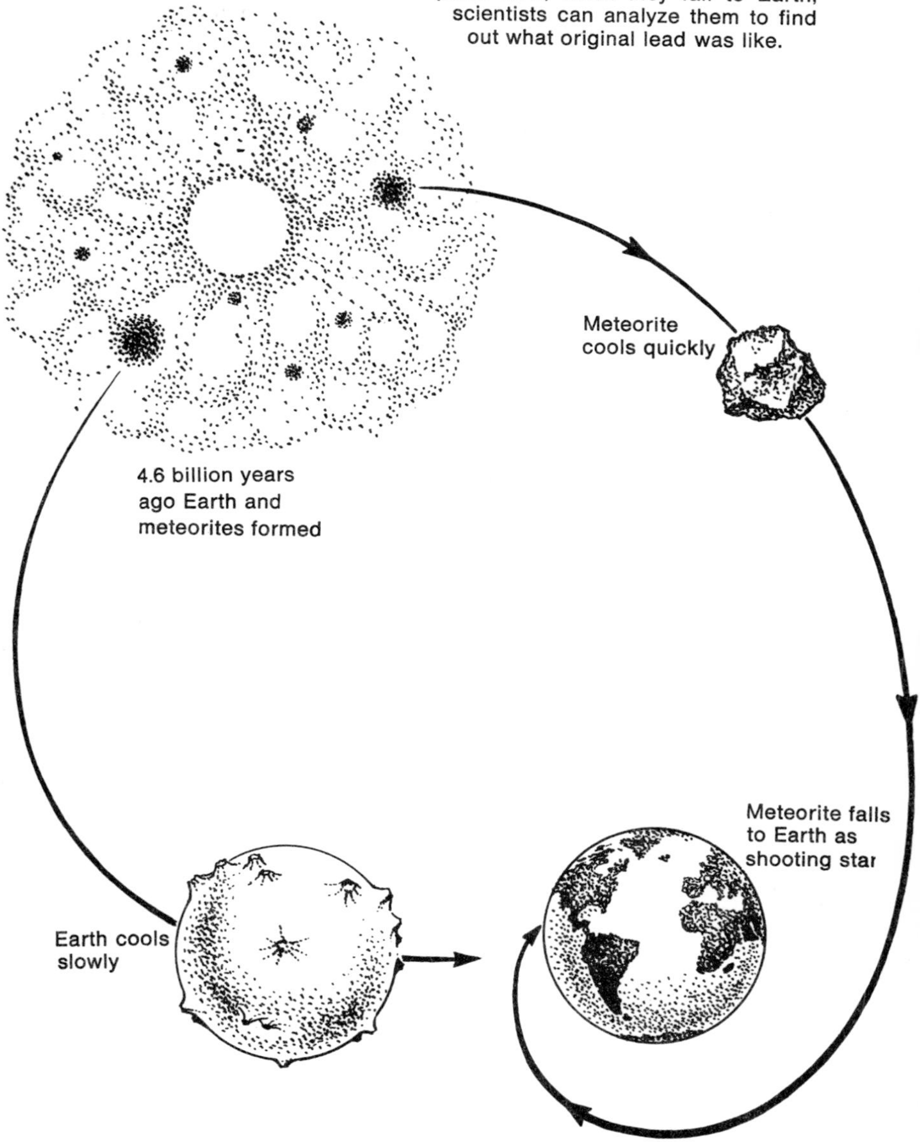

Meteorite cools quickly

4.6 billion years ago Earth and meteorites formed

Meteorite falls to Earth as shooting star

Earth cools slowly

chemist, suggested it should be possible to find samples of the original lead of the solar system in meteorites. Meteorites are bits of rock orbiting around the Sun just like the Earth. Quite often they get pulled in by the Earth's gravity, glowing red-hot through friction as they rush through the atmosphere, and appearing to us as shooting stars. Scientists can analyze meteorites that are not completely burned away as they fall. Dr. Brown's idea was that in certain types of meteorites there should be pure, original lead — lead that had never been added to by radioactivity since the Earth and all the rest of the solar system first were formed (Fig. 3).

Unfortunately, the first time he tried to find lead in a suitable meteorite and to measure the proportion of the isotopes in it, he could not detect anything at all, except the tiny amount of lead in the chemicals used for the analysis.

Not until six years later, after a special lead-free laboratory had been built in California, did anyone succeed in isolating lead from a meteorite. The meteorite turned out to have only three atoms of lead to every million other atoms. But there was one atom of lead-204 to every nine of lead-206 — twice as much lead-204 by proportion as there is in most lead found in the Earth's rocks today. In other words, only about half the lead-206 found on Earth has been there since the beginning. The rest has gradually been built up by radioactivity.

From then on it was fairly easy to work out how long this must have taken. The answer was the 4.6 billion years now accepted as the age of the Earth. This age has since been confirmed by measurements on other meteorites.

"Clocks" and fossils

Many millions of years after the Earth began, life appeared in the oceans and slowly evolved into what we know today.

Geologists were able to recognize different periods in the Earth's history by examining rocks and the fossils in them long before they could say just when these periods began and ended. Only when scientists started using radioactivity as a clock was it possible to put firm dates to rocks.

The dates given to the Earth's rocks are the combined result of thousands of different radioactivity measurements, each one a difficult job which must be done very carefully. First of all the scientist must find rock which contains a measurable quantity of radioisotope. Almost all volcanic rocks include enough uranium or thorium to be measured by modern techniques, although the amount is very small by ordinary standards. In each ton of granite, for example, there is usually about one-tenth of an ounce of uranium — say, three parts in a million.

Once a suitable rock sample has been chosen it has to be crushed to a fine sand, separated out almost grain by grain, and then treated with the purest possible chemicals to extract the lead and uranium. The proportions of the different isotopes are measured with an instrument called a *mass spectrometer,* which separates them out with electric and magnetic fields.

Sometimes it is possible to measure the age of a piece of rock in several different ways, if it contains both uranium and thorium. Then all three radioisotopes and their daughters, as well as the relative proportions of the lead isotopes, provide separate clocks. The amount of helium present can sometimes be used as a measure of the rock's age as well, although naturally the gas tends to escape from rocks in the course of millions of years. These different ages often disagree, but between them they give a good average.

Other radioisotopes have been used as clocks, too. One of

them is rubidium-87, which has a very long half-life of 48 billion years and turns into strontium-87 as the daughter isotope. Another important one is potassium-40 which decays to argon-40 (a gas) or calcium-40. Both rubidium and potassium provide a useful way of dating sedimentary rocks, which rarely include much uranium or thorium.

It is important to be able to date sedimentary rocks because they usually contain fossils of extinct animals and plants. If geologists can find out when the fossils were alive they can straightway tell the age of other rocks that include the same kind of fossils. A whole science, called *stratigraphy,* has grown up, concerned with working out when various extinct creatures were alive and using their fossils to find out what period rocks and geographical features such as mountains date from.

The sort of fossils they use most for this work are not the remains of giant dinosaurs or other strange creatures, because these are rare, but minute things which often can be seen only through a microscope. These microfossils (Fig. 4) are the remains of tiny single-celled sea creatures, or sometimes of pollen from ancient plants. There may be thousands of them in a few grains of rock. What is more, they are found everywhere and in all kinds of rock — in sandstone, limestone, flint — and even in oil. This means they provide the ideal clues for identifying and comparing rocks from different periods.

The scars of time

The "scars" left by radioactivity in crystals provide an entirely different way of measuring time, discovered only recently. When a radioactive atom breaks up it releases a lot of energy and the fragments fly off like bullets. For example, an atomic bomb explosion is the result of many billions of uranium atoms breaking up in this way in a very short time. In a rock crystal there is often a sprinkling of radioactive atoms. The energy liberated when one of them breaks up is much too small for us to notice directly, of course, but the fragments cut short trails of damage through the crystal.

A few years ago three American scientists decided to see if they could find these tracks left by tiny atomic "explosions" millions of years ago. Any natural crystal such as quartz or mica should be marked with *fission tracks,* as they are called, if it contains radioactive material. In 1962 the team managed to see tracks in mica, a flaky mineral. They did this by first

FIG. 4. These are some of the microscopic fossil plants geologists use to help them date rocks. They are only one- or two-thousandths of an inch across.

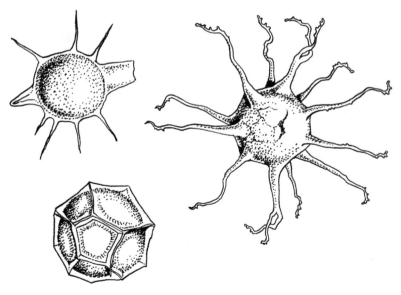

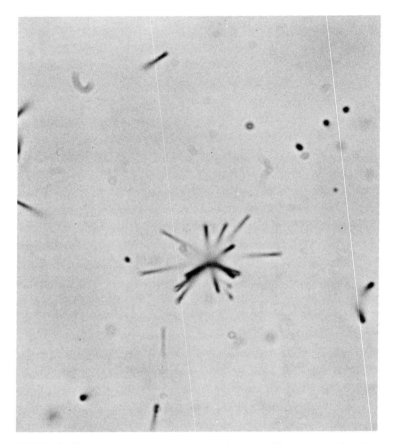

PHOTO 1. Fission tracks left in a crystal by a million years of radioactive bombardment can be etched out so as to be visible under the microscope, as in this piece of mica.

etching the tracks out with a strong acid to enlarge them, and then looking at them through a microscope (Photo 1). They found they could count each individual track in this way, although it was a long and difficult job.

Then, after finding out how much uranium or thorium there was in the crystal, they could work out how long it must have taken for that number of tracks to accumulate. This told them how long the crystal had been in existence, collecting and preserving its scars.

Counting fission tracks is expected to be particularly useful for finding the ages of fairly young rocks — rocks less than 100 million years old. It has been used chiefly on crystals such as quartz or some semiprecious stones, but it can also be applied to man-made glass. Glass often includes quite a large amount of uranium, so, even though it is new compared with rock crystals, much old glassware already contains a considerable number of tracks.

Counting year by year

Trying to weigh a grain of sand on scales meant for truckloads would be a waste of effort; and the same applies to measuring time. Radioactive clocks which can span billions of years are just not sensitive enough to help us with the dates of human history, going back only a few thousand years. The potassium-argon clock is useful up to about half a million years ago, and fission track dating can measure times of only a few hundred years, but generally when we want to date prehistoric human remains we have to turn to other methods.

There are several to choose from, although it is not often possible to date a particular relic in more than one way. Some of the simplest are also the most accurate, because they are just a matter of counting the number of years since an event took place. Everyone knows that the number of rings in the trunk of a tree gives its age in years. Each spring and summer a tree grows a new layer of wood, but the wood grown late in the season is often darker than the rest, and so a ring is visible when the trunk is cut across. Each year leaves its mark on the tree in this way. Even these familiar tree rings can sometimes provide a way of dating the past.

Tree rings are not all of the same thickness. In a good year all trees will put on thick rings but in a bad year — one with very little rain, for instance — the rings will be very thin. You can see this for yourself on any sawed-off tree trunk.

So what the archaeologist has to do is to work out the succession of good years and bad years, usually by looking at tree rings whose age is already known or can be found in other ways. Then when he wants to date a particular piece of wood, perhaps from a building he is interested in, it has to be cut and treated to reveal the rings of the tree it originally came from. All being well, it will be possible to match up the thick and thin rings with the succession of good and bad years already worked out (Fig. 5). This tells him when the tree was alive and growing, from which he can draw conclusions about the age of the building.

Tree ring dating has been used a lot for American Indian buildings 500 to 1,000 years old, built before the Europeans had even discovered the continent. In Europe there is not so much use for it because there are usually written records and so on extending back much further than tree ring dating can go. But the same idea of matching up a succession of wet and dry years with the traces left behind them is used in other ways.

One thing that has left an annual mark in the soil of Europe is the retreat of the glaciers as the last Ice Age ended.

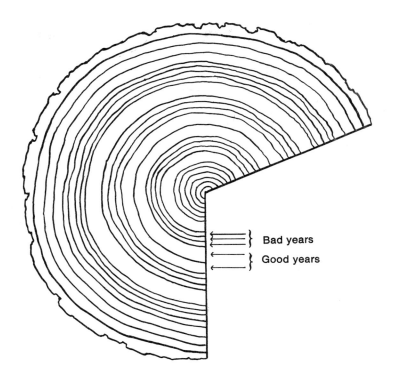

Bad years

Good years

FIG. 5. Tree rings are thick or thin according to whether it was a good, bad or average year for tree growth when they were formed. The pattern of good and bad years can be matched up between different pieces of wood and used to help find how old they are.

Each summer some of the ice would melt and trickle down through crevasses to form a great river rushing under the glaciers. All sorts of stones and sand and clay would be swept away in the river and deposited as a thin layer where the glaciers ended in the sea or a lake (Fig. 6). With the winter the river would cease to flow, but each spring it began again,

29

FIG. 6. a. Each summer, as the glaciers retreated after the Ice Age, clay and sand were washed away by streams from the melting ice.
b. All this debris settled in a thin layer at the bottom of the lakes which usually formed at the foot of the glaciers.
c. Every year a new layer was formed, stretching a little farther north each time.
d. When the glaciers eventually disappeared they left a whole series of these layers, called *varves,* behind them. Now people can dig down and count them to find out how many years the glaciers took to retreat. (There would actually be many more varves, each one much thinner than are shown in the drawing.)

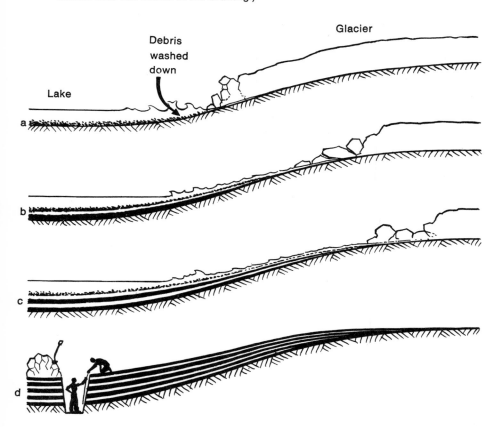

leaving a new layer of sand and clay stretching a bit farther to the north each time the glaciers retreated.

These yearly layers of clay, called *varves,* can still be seen in many places. The first man to realize they could be used, like tree rings, for counting years, was a Swedish geologist, Baron Gerard De Geer. There are usually only a few hundred varves visible at one place; farther to the north there are newer varves, to the south older ones. To build up a complete series of varves, De Geer obtained measurements at hundreds of points on a line from north to south through Sweden. Then he fitted them all together by matching up particular years which, because of an unusually warm summer that melted a lot of ice, showed very thick varves.

In the end he was able to build up a complete series spanning 5,000 years, the time it took for the ice to retreat from the southern tip of Sweden to the year when the glaciers in the Swedish mountains were separated from the main ice cap to the north. This was a big step in the retreat of the ice, and there must have been huge floods that year in Sweden because the varve it left behind is very thick.

Later on, De Geer and other geologists managed to work out the date of the splitting of the ice cap, partly by counting more than 7,000 varves in a layer of sediment a hundred feet thick under a lake which had been drained. Now geologists are able to say that the Swedish ice cap split off from the main one in the year 6839 B.C. With this year as a fixed point, each stage in the retreat of the ice can be timed very precisely.

All kinds of things show a yearly cycle, besides tree rings and varves. Oysters, for example, show their age by the number of rings on their shells. And recently it was discovered, in

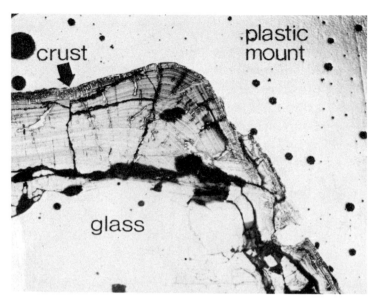

PHOTO 2. a. Old glass grows a crust which can be seen quite clearly in this microscope picture of a fragment of glass from the Middle Ages.

PHOTO 2. b. Magnified sixty times, the yearly layers in this crust can easily be seen and counted to find out how old the glass is.

the laboratories of a modern glass firm, that old glass which has been buried or under water grows a kind of crust which has yearly layers in it. The layers can be seen under a powerful microscope (Photo 2), and they may also provide a useful way of dating.

Climate as a clock

When people first started to study prehistoric man, they came up against the same difficulty that faced the geologists in their studies of the Earth. There was usually no way to tell the age of the tools and other relics left by our ancestors. Different primitive cultures could be identified and divided up into periods such as the Stone Age, Bronze Age and so on, much as the geologist does with rocks and fossils. Sometimes a lucky joint find of prehistoric remains together with something that could be dated — coins for example — revealed the age of the remains, but that was all.

Baron De Geer's clay varve counting was the first exact method discovered of measuring prehistoric time. Its disadvantage is that human settlements were naturally some distance from the glaciers, so their remains cannot be dated directly from varves. Archaeologists could get around this by using what the varves did tell them — where the edge of the ice was at different times — to work out what the climate must have been like in the lands to the south. Then from the remains found in prehistoric settlements it was often possible to guess what the local climate had been like when men had lived there, and so make an estimate of how long ago that was.

It was another Swede, Lennart Von Post, who took the guesswork out of this process and made it into an accurate way of measuring time. He started from the discovery that peat contains innumerable tiny but perfectly preserved grains of tree pollen. Peat is a spongy soil which is an early stage in the conversion of trees and other plants into coal. It covers many areas left waterlogged or as shallow lakes by the Ice Age glaciers, and it has a way of preserving all kinds of things, particularly pollen which is very tough-skinned in any case.

What Von Post did was to examine samples of peat under the microscope. He found he could count the number of grains of pollen from each kind of tree. Peat laid down soon after the ice had retreated contained a lot of birch pollen, he discovered. Later on, as the climate got warmer, pine woods replaced the birch trees, followed later still by oak and then beech. All these changes were faithfully recorded in the peat by the pollen from the trees each spring.

All that was necessary to find out what the climate was like at a particular time and place was to take a few grains of peat from the spot — perhaps actually from a tool to be dated. Then the number of grains of pollen in the peat from each different kind of tree had to be counted up and compared with special charts prepared by Von Post, to find out what kind of climate the sample had come from. From there it was a simple step, with the help of De Geer's dates for the retreat of the ice, to find the age of the peat and whatever remains there were in it.

Lennart Von Post announced his discovery in 1916, and eventually it became possible to date prehistoric finds by pollen counts to within one year in ten either way. Pollen counts are still a very important way of studying the past, but their disadvantage as a way of measuring time is that they are useless without some other way of dating the actual changes in climate. Not until after the Second World War was a way found of dating prehistoric remains which gave their age independently of all other methods.

From the moment of death   1475048

The discovery that all living things have a sort of built-in "clock" which starts ticking only at the moment of death made it much easier to date prehistoric remains. The idea came from Willard F. Libby, an atomic chemist in the University of Chicago, who had worked on the project to build the first atomic bombs. Not surprisingly, the idea depends on radioactivity, like so many other ways of measuring time. In this case it is the tiny but detectable amount of radioactivity in all living things.

This radioactivity is given off by an isotope called carbon-14, which is continuously being made in the air by the action of cosmic rays from space on carbon dioxide gas. All living things are based on the element carbon, so they take in some carbon-14 along with ordinary carbon as a matter of course. As fast as the carbon-14 decays it is replaced from outside, so all living things end up with about the same proportion of carbon-14 in them — one atom to every trillion atoms of ordinary carbon.

When an animal or plant dies it no longer converts carbon to living tissues, of course. The carbon-14 already present begins slowly to dwindle away by the ordinary process of radioactive decay. Dr. Libby realized that, because of this progressive decay after death, the amount of radioactivity remaining in a dead animal or plant will depend on how long it has been dead. Carbon-14 has a half-life of 5,568 years, so a piece of wood that is only half as radioactive as a living tree must have been cut down about 5,568 years ago.

To test his idea, Libby and a special committee of four

archaeologists began by trying to measure the age of material which had already been dated in other ways. They took radio-activity measurements of wood from the graves of Egyptian pharaohs and ashes from the camps of Roman armies. Each time the carbon-14 age came out to within 10 percent of the age already known.

Since then *radiocarbon or carbon-14 dating,* as it is called, has been used a lot. It is now the most usual way of dating any human or animal remains less than 20,000 years old. Further back than that difficulties arise because the amount of carbon-14 still surviving in such long-dead things is very small. So far radiocarbon has given us the date for such things as the oldest agricultural settlements in the Middle East (about 6700 B.C.), the people who probably created the beautiful wall paintings of animals in the caves of Lascaux in France (about 15,000 B.C), and the oldest settlement of the Australian aborigines yet discovered (about 1000 B.C). It is far from being perfectly accurate yet, but it is the best way we have of dating the recent past.

Who wants to know?

So far this book has been about the ways scientists have found of measuring time that has passed; in other words, of finding out how long ago things happened. Men have not put so much ingenuity into discovering such things just for the sake of the knowledge itself. The information is essential to many different sciences.

Knowing when the aborigines first arrived in Australia, or when men first started to grow crops is very important to understanding the history of mankind. Historians must have these dates to trace the movements of different peoples across the world and the rise of the first civilizations.

In the same way biologists need dates to study the development of plants and animals. The idea of evolution from lower forms of life to more complicated ones has become one of the foundations of biology since Charles Darwin first suggested it in 1858. The dates found from the rocks tell biologists how long different fossils took to evolve as living matter and die out again, and gives them a framework upon which to hang their theories.

Geologists need dates as well, to write the history of the rocks. And sometimes it is very important for them to know whether events in different parts of the world happened at the same time. Did the Ice Ages come at the same time in Europe and the Antarctic, for example? Or was one continent cold while the other remained warm? Deciding between different explanations of the cause of the Ice Ages depends partly on the answer to this question. Radiocarbon dating has already shown that the cold periods probably occurred at the same time north and south of the equator. To take another problem, fission track dating has been used to show that strange glassy pebbles called *tektites* found in various parts of the world probably came from meteorites. It was done by showing that the tektites had exactly the same ages as rocks known to have been made by the great heat of meteorites crashing on the Earth.

Geophysicists, too, who study the interior of the Earth, need to know how old it is to help formulate their theories. If they know how long the Earth's interior has been cooling, they can tell how hot it must have been to start with; or if it began cold and was heated up later by energy liberated by radioactivity. And for astronomers studying the stars it is important to know the age of the Sun, the nearest star of all.

Finally, if only we knew more exactly how old the elements are, we might be able to say much more about the way they were formed. Did it happen all at once, or were they slowly built up over a long period? Better measurements of their age will help us to find the answer.

2 Calendars and clocks

Dividing up time

Men have always had three natural "clocks" to tell them the time. These are the seasons, and the different pattern of stars that goes with each one; the changing face of the Moon; and the movement of the Sun across the sky.

These three clocks provide the three basic units for dividing up time — the year, the (lunar) month, and the day. For tens of thousands of years they were the only clocks and the only units that were needed. They told early man when to head for home so as not to get caught by nightfall, or when to set out after migrating herds of animals. They are still the only ways of measuring time known to millions of primitive people in the world.

These three natural clocks divide up time by endlessly repeating the same motion. The Earth revolves on its axis, so that during the day the Sun seems to be moving across the sky, and at night the stars apparently do the same. The Moon goes around the Earth, changing from "full" when the Sun is shining on its earthward face to "new" when its darkened side is toward the Earth, and back again. The whole cycle takes 29½ days.

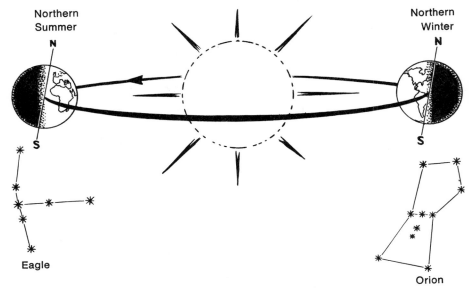

Northern
Summer

Northern
Winter

Eagle

Orion

FIG. 7. As the Earth goes around the Sun the side away from it — the
night side — faces toward different parts of the sky, with different stars.

The Earth goes around the Sun in just under 365¼ days,
so that in each season the night side of our world faces toward
a different part of the sky, revealing different stars (Fig. 7).
How these natural clocks were fitted together into our present
calendar is one of the subjects of this part of the book. The
other is how people learned to measure time more accurately
than anything else.

Besides the year, the month and the day, the astronomer
priests of early civilizations were able to divide up the times
of light and darkness into hours with the help of sundials and
instruments for observing the stars. When their instruments
became good enough they could even measure the amount a
star moved across the sky in a minute of time. But they could

not build clocks to show hours and minutes accurately — let alone seconds — because they had nothing that could be made to pace out time with a regularly repeated motion. Instead they had to use water trickling through a hole or the burning of a candle for a "clock" — things which moved at a steady rate instead of being regularly repeated. The trouble was, such things were never quite steady enough.

Only in the seventeenth century, when the telescope and the pendulum clock were invented, could scientists start to measure time in minutes and seconds. But the basic units were still the year and the day, although by that time people had stopped taking much account of the Moon's phases.

The second was defined as one 86,400th part of *the mean solar day.* The mean solar day is the average time between the Sun being at its highest point in the sky on one day and when it reaches its peak again next day. It has to be the average, as the exact length of solar day is different at different times of year, because the Earth's orbit around the Sun is not exactly circular.

To make things still more confusing, the solar day is about four minutes longer than the *sidereal day,* which is the time the stars take to return to the same position in the sky from night to night. This difference occurs because the Earth is traveling around the Sun as well as spinning on its own axis.

Eventually, as clocks grew ever more accurate, astronomers discovered that the speed at which the Earth turns is itself varying, so that the length of the mean solar day varies as well. Although this difference is only a few parts in a hundred million every year, it is too much for modern scientists to ignore. The second had to be defined again. In 1956 the International Committee of Weights and Measures declared the second equal to one 31,556,925.9747th part of the year A.D. 1900.

Soon even this was not precise enough, because atomic clocks are now being made which are more regular, and therefore more accurate timekeepers, than the movement of the Earth itself. In 1964 the second was officially defined as the time it takes for a cesium atom to vibrate in a certain way 9,192,631,770 times. This means that scientists can now measure time more accurately than anything else.

Calendars in stone

Men were already recording the phases of the Moon more than 30,000 years ago. Over a thousand sets of scratches on bone or ivory or simple paintings on cave walls have been found that are now thought to be the work of Ice Age Moon-watchers. Judging from the scratches they knew that the Moon takes 29½ days to go through all its phases. These are the first astronomical observations and the first measurements of time that we know anything about. The two things have been closely connected ever since.

Much later men began to settle down as farmers. They no longer needed to know so urgently when the full Moon would light up the night for hunting, but they had to have a proper yearly calendar to tell them when to sow their crops. The priests had the job of keeping the calendar, by observing the shifting pattern of the stars and the position of sunrise on particular days. Eventually observatories were built of standing stones to mark out the seasons and probably to serve as temples too. The most famous of them is Stonehenge, a group of massive stones erected by the prehistoric inhabitants of Britain on Salisbury Plain in Wiltshire.

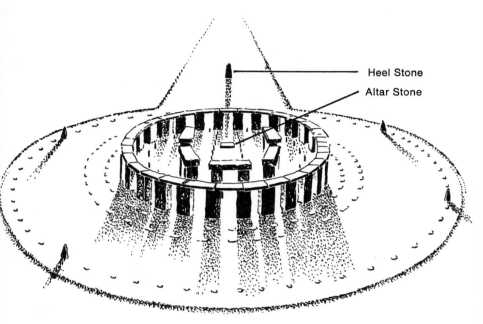

Heel Stone

Altar Stone

FIG. 8. This drawing shows how Stonehenge looked when it was complete. Seen from the Altar Stone, the Sun rises almost exactly over the Heel Stone on Midsummer Morning.

Stonehenge is surrounded by an earth rampart about 150 yards across. Inside is a circle of standing stones, and inside that is yet another set of stones, arranged as a horseshoe (Fig. 8). Right in the middle is a flat boulder, often called the Altar Stone. Looking from the Altar Stone through the open end of the horseshoe and a gap in the earth rampart you can see the Heel Stone standing by itself about 100 yards away. Seen from the Altar, the Sun rises almost exactly over the Heel Stone on Midsummer Morning.

When Stonehenge was first built, about 1800 B.C., the Midsummer Sun did rise exactly over the Heel Stone. But because the Earth is wobbling slowly in space, taking 25,800 years to complete a wobble, the position of the Midsummer sunrise has shifted slightly since then.

Great stone monuments like Stonehenge but not quite so impressive are to be found all over Britain and western France. Almost all of them point to the Midsummer or Midwinter sunrise, or else to sunrise on some other special date. This shows that the late Stone Age and Bronze Age men who built them knew how many days there are in a year.

According to a theory put forward by Professor Gerald Hawkins of Harvard University, Stonehenge was even used to predict eclipses of the Moon. If this is true its builders must have known of the cycle of 18 years and 8 months in which the pattern of lunar eclipses repeats itself. This has always been called the *Metonic Cycle,* after the ancient Greek scientist Meton who is supposed to have discovered it about 430 B.C. It now seems that men may have known about it long before that date.

Even before Stonehenge was built, the astronomer priests of Babylon and Egypt were observing the Moon, the stars and the planets, and working out the beginnings of our calendar. To the Egyptians the most important star was Sirius, the brightest one in the sky. Sirius rises at sunset about the beginning of January and just a few minutes before sunrise in July. In Egypt this rising with the Sun marked the beginning of the new year. It also signaled the coming of the annual floods of the River Nile, which are still essential to the fertility of the fields for many hundreds of miles along the river.

The importance of Sirius was marked in stone as well. The famous Great Pyramid of Cheops, built about 2700 B.C., was arranged so that when the star was at its highest point in the sky its light shone straight down a passage, into the royal burial chamber within the pyramid. But the slow wobbling of the Earth, mentioned earlier, has tipped the passage out of line today.

A difficult problem for the early calendar makers was to fit the lunar month of 29½ days into the year of 365¼ days. One solution was to have a year of only 354 days, or exactly 12 lunar months. This means that if the beginning of one year is in midwinter, 16 years later New Year's Day will have slipped back to midsummer. In spite of this drawback Mohammedan countries still use a 354-day year.

But the Ancient Egyptians went on to construct a calendar with twelve months, each 30 days long, making 360 days, with an extra five added on to make the year up to 365 days. Later on they started to add another extra day every four years to allow for the odd quarter day in the length of the year. We still use the same system by having a leap year every fourth year, giving February an extra day that year.

Prince Amenemhet's clock

Once people began to live in towns, they began to need to know the time of day, as well as having a calendar. They had to fix the hours of work and the time for public entertainments or religious ceremonies. From telling the time by the movement of the Sun across the sky it was probably an easy step to mark where the shadow of a tree or rock fell at different times of the day, and so make the first sundial. We have many examples of sundials used in ancient Egypt. Some were quite small and portable, like the one shown in Fig. 9. Others took the form of massive monuments or buildings.

But the hours shown by these early sundials were not the

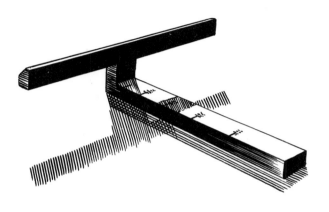

FIG. 9. Some ancient Egyptian sundials were quite small, like this one. It had to be turned around at midday, and the six hours into which the Egyptians divided the morning and the afternoon were marked off on the base.

same as the ones we use now. The day, from sunrise to sunset, was divided into twelve equal hours, so that midday fell at the sixth hour. In summer, when the days were longer, the hours were longer too, while the shorter days of winter had twelve shorter hours.

It sounds an awkward way to count time, but in the days when people got up at sunrise and went to bed soon after sunset it was quite sensible and workable. The system was

FIG. 10. The water clock Amenemhet made for King Amenophis was probably very like this one, with raised scales on the inside, so that the king could tell the time in the dark by touch.

used all over the ancient world, and in Europe right up to the end of the Middle Ages. The night was also divided into twelve equal hours, and the astronomer priests made instruments for telling the time at night by observing the stars.

An Egyptian inscription written about 1500 B.C. tells how a Prince Amenemhet made a water clock for his king, Amenophis I, intended for telling the time at night. It was similar to the one in the sketch (Fig. 10), shaped like a big bucket.

At nightfall it was filled with water, which trickled out slowly through a small hole near the bottom. King Amenophis could tell the time from the level the water had fallen to, and in the dark he could read the hour by touch from scales marked inside the bucket. There was a different hour scale for each month of the year, to allow for the changing length of the hours.

Although the idea is simple, Amenemhet must have gone to a lot of trouble to get his clock working properly. First of all, he had to allow for the fact that water would be forced out of the hole more quickly when the clock was full than later on in the night when it was almost empty, and the pressure much less. This is why the clock had to have sloping sides.

Allowing for changes in temperature was harder. The biggest drawback of water clocks is that water flows more slowly when cool than when heated, so the clock runs too fast in hot weather, too slow if it is frosty. Probably Amenemhet adjusted the slope of his clock's sides a little to allow for the water in it cooling during the night, but this is not good enough to permit use of the clock at all times of day.

The temperature problem was never solved, although the Romans and the Arabs made much more complicated water clocks later on. In the Middle Ages water clocks were used in many monasteries. The times for prayers and meals were strictly laid down, so the monks had to have a clock of some kind, and since their day began before dawn in the winter a sundial was not enough. But for most people sundials remained the only way of telling the time, and quite adequate for their needs.

The balance, rod and crown

No one knows when the first mechanical, clockwork-driven clock was made, or who made it, or where he lived. It is difficult to tell what sort of timekeeper old documents are referring to when they speak of clocks because they used the same Latin word *horologium* for all kinds. For example, St. Paul's Cathedral in London already had some kind of clock in 1286 because a man called Bartholomew the Orologius was given a loaf of bread and an allowance of beer every day for looking after it.

It seems likely, however, that the first mechanical clocks were made about the year 1300 in northern Italy or southern Germany. Certainly craftsmen were beginning to learn the skills needed for clockmaking then. Metal workers were beginning to make cast iron, the material that most early clocks were made from. Various new inventions appeared in Europe about that time, such as spectacles and guns. Clockwork of a sort was already being made to drive "automatons," which were mechanical moving figures. Automatons can still be seen on some old clocks such as the one at Rye in the south of England, where two mechanical men strike bells at the hours and quarters (Photo 3a).

But all these machines lacked a way of controlling the speed at which the clockwork moved. The unknown man who found a way to do this by using what we now call a *verge escapement* was the real inventor of the clock.

To understand why an escapement is needed, let us consider how those early clocks worked. Like many that are still in use, they were driven by a weight on a string. The string was wrapped around a cylinder with the weight hanging down. As the weight descended it pulled the cylinder around and turned the hands of the clock. Obviously the weight could not be allowed to fall without some restraint or the clock would just run very fast for a moment, then stop. There had to be a mechanism that would allow the cylinder to turn a little bit at a time and no more.

This is what the escapement did. The cylinder was made to turn a wheel shaped rather like a king's crown. A rod with

PHOTO 3. a. Automatons can still be seen in some old clocks, such as this one on the tower of St. Mary's Church at Rye, England, where two mechanical men strike bells at the hours and quarters.

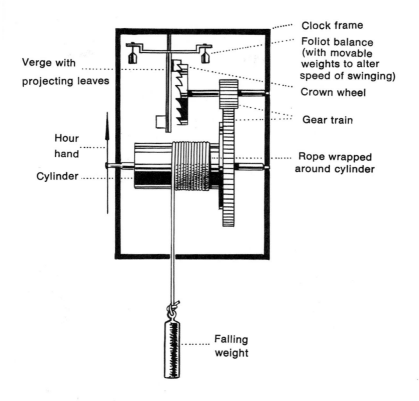

Verge with
projecting leaves

Hour
hand

Cylinder

Clock frame

Foliot balance
(with movable
weights to alter
speed of swinging)

Crown wheel

Gear train

Rope wrapped
around cylinder

Falling
weight

FIG. 11. Simplified version of an early clock.

metal leaves sticking out from it, called a verge, was arranged
to catch the teeth of this crown wheel as it turned and allow
only one tooth to escape at a time (Fig. 11).

The verge was also attached to a weighted metal beam
called a *foliot balance,* which was kept swinging backward
and forward. At each swing the balance moved the verge, to
release one more tooth of the crown wheel. In this way the
time it took the foliot balance to swing controlled the turning

PHOTO 3. b. Most of the earliest clocks, like this one from Wells Cathedral in England, were installed in public places. At the top left you can see the clock's only hand, for indicating the hour, and below it the weighted rope wrapped around a cylinder which drove the works.

of the crown wheel, which in turn, with the help of a train of gears, controlled the speed of the clock.

In this way time was measured out by a regularly repeated motion. This is what distinguished these first mechanical clocks from all earlier timekeepers, and made them the true ancestors of the clocks and watches we use today.

PHOTO 4. Many portable sundials, like this one, included compass needles so that they could be faced in the right direction.

Time for ordinary people

The first mechanical clocks were much too big, bulky and expensive for ordinary people's homes. Most were installed in public places such as cathedral towers. Three clocks made about 1390 for the cathedrals of Salisbury and Wells in England and Rouen in France still exist (Photo 3b). All these early clocks had only an hour hand, perhaps with the dial marked to show quarter hours as well. Since they could keep time only to within 10 or 20 minutes a day (with regular attention from a professional clock winder), there was not much point in having a minute hand.

For centuries after mechanical clocks were first invented, ordinary people continued to use sundials if they needed to know the time. Some very beautiful portable ones were made. They included compass needles, so that the sundial could be faced in the right direction (Photo 4). Increasing knowledge of astronomy made it possible to construct more accurate sundials, and the old system of dividing the day and the night each into 12 equal hours gradually gave way to the modern 24-hour day.

At the same time clocks gradually became smaller and cheaper. Spring-driven clocks were made, and watches began to appear from about 1500 (Photo 5a). But there was not much improvement in accuracy until the invention of the pendulum clock.

The great Italian scientist Galileo Galilei noticed in 1582 that a pendulum always takes the same length of time to swing. He realized that if a pendulum could be linked with a clock and made to control its speed, the clock should run very accurately.

Galileo and his son Vicenzio studied the problem of making a clock mechanism to count the swings of a pendulum and keep them going. But it was not until 1656 that another great scientist, the Dutchman Christiaan Huygens, made a successful pendulum clock.

Before long, pendulum clocks were being made that were accurate to within ten seconds a day. The pendulum quickly

PHOTO 5. a. Early watches, like this English one from about 1630, usually had only an hour hand.

replaced the foliot balance and, after centuries of use, the verge escapement also gave way to a variety of better escapements. Clockmaking made rapid progress, and many of the beautiful grandfather clocks, built from the eighteenth century onward, with a long case to contain the pendulum, are still working well.

Pope Gregory puts the clock right

Julius Caesar is famous for many things, but his most lasting action was to have the calendar reorganized. In 44 B.C. he asked an astronomer called Sosigenes from Alexandria — a great center of learning then — to draw up a new calendar. The various calendars then in use in different parts of the Roman Empire had become very confused by attempts to fit the lunar months into the year.

Sosigenes gave up trying to match lunar months with calendar ones. He drew up the system of months we still use, with an extra day in February every four years to allow for the odd quarter day in the Earth's journey around the Sun. One of the months was named July, after Julius Caesar; and soon afterward the next one was called August, after his successor, Augustus.

The Julian Calendar, as it was called, was a good one and it was used unchanged for 1,600 years. But it was like a clock which runs a little slow — because the year is not exactly 365¼ days, as Sosigenes believed, but is actually 365 days 5 hours 48 minutes and 46 seconds long. So the Julian Calendar fell 11 minutes and 14 seconds behind every year, which put it a whole day behind after 128 years.

By the year 1581 the calendar had fallen 13 days behind, which was making the dates of religious festivals such as Easter badly wrong. So Pope Gregory XIII asked another astronomer, Clavius, to work out how this could be put right. Clavius suggested first that ten days should be dropped out of one year, to bring the date back to what it was in A.D. 325, the year when the date of Easter was finally fixed.

Then, so that the calendar would not go awry again, he suggested there should be fewer leap years to bring the average length of the calendar year down closer to the true length. Instead of all years that could be divided by four being leap years (1580, 1584, 1588, and so on), those that could be divided by 100 as well (1700, 1800) would be ordinary years, unless they could also be divided by 400 (1600, 2000), in which case they would stay as leap years. In other words, the year 1900 would not be a leap year but the year 2000 would be.

Pope Gregory decreed that these suggestions should be adopted. In Catholic countries the day after October 4, 1582, was October 15. But many non-Catholic countries such as England refused to accept this reform for a long time. Not until 1751 did Parliament pass an act to bring Britain into line with the rest of Europe. By then it was necessary to drop 11 days, and September 2, 1752, was followed by September 14.

At this there were riots in many parts of the country, because people thought they had been cheated of 11 days of their lives. They had not lost anything at all, of course, any more than you do if you move the hands of a clock. It will be a long time before any more changes are necessary because the Gregorian Calendar, as it is called, loses only one day in 3,000 years.

The $50,000 problem

Sailors have a good reason for wanting accurate clocks. They need to know the time to help them find their position at sea. The method of finding a ship's *latitude* (how far north of the equator it is) from the height of the Pole Star in the sky was known in medieval times. The Pole Star's elevation above the horizon, as measured in degrees at a particular spot on the

Earth's surface, gives the latitude of that spot in degrees quite accurately.

But there was no such simple way of finding a ship's *longitude* — how far to the east or west — without an accurate way of measuring time. Craftsmen tried to make a clock which would keep good time at sea for more than 200 years before they succeeded.

To understand why such a clock was needed, you must try to imagine the Earth and the Sun in space. It is easy to see that the side of the Earth facing the Sun is in daylight while the other side is in darkness. When it is exactly noon in one place it is midnight on the opposite side of the world, 180 degrees of longitude away. In other words, a difference of 180 degrees of longitude means a 12-hour difference in time, or 15 degrees means a one-hour time difference (Fig. 12).

Each degree of longitude has its own local time and it is not difficult for a navigator to find out what it is by observing the Sun or the stars. Then, if he knows what the local time is somewhere else, at the Royal Observatory at Greenwich near London, for instance, the time difference tells him how many degrees and fractions of a degree he lies to the east or west of that spot.

The problem was to make a clock which would still show *Greenwich time* to within a minute or so after a long sea voyage. Early clocks had to be put right every day from sundials which, of course, could show only local time. Even pendulum clocks and spring-driven watches with balance wheels were not good enough to stand all the shocks and temperature changes they would encounter at sea.

Astronomers tried to find ways of calculating Greenwich time from the position of the planets or the phases of the

FIG. 12. When it is noon in Greenwich, near London, it is six o'clock in the morning in New Orleans and midnight in the Fiji Islands.

Moon — in fact, the Greenwich Observatory was founded in 1675 by King Charles II to find ways of doing this. But the observations and calculations needed were too difficult and complicated to be done at sea, so sailors just had to try to work out how far to the east or west they had gone by estimating the ship's speed.

In 1714 the British government offered a prize of $50,000 to anyone who could make a clock that would be no more than two minutes wrong after a voyage from Britain to Jamaica in the West Indies. In spite of the prize — a huge amount in those days — no one could meet these conditions for nearly fifty years. The problem was eventually solved by

59

a Yorkshire carpenter called John Harrison, who devoted most of his life to it.

Between 1728 and 1759 Harrison built four timekeepers or *chronometers,* all using balance wheels and designed to accommodate temperature changes. The fourth, much smaller than the others (only five inches across), was triumphantly successful. In 1761 his son William took this chronometer (Photo 5b) to Jamaica in H.M.S. *Deptford.* When it arrived at the island, after 161 days at sea, the chronometer was only five seconds in error — good enough to give the ship's position to within 1½ miles. Even so, it took several years and a lot of bitter wrangling before John Harrison managed to get all the prize money due to him.

Strangely enough, Harrison's design was not actually used for practical chronometers — for one thing, it was too expensive. Modern chronometers owe more to a cheaper and simpler design produced by a Frenchman, Pierre Le Roy, soon after Harrison's success. By the end of the eighteenth century chronometers were being manufactured for reasonable sums, making navigation much easier and safer.

Setting the time standards

Once accurate clocks were generally available, cities started to fix their time by law. As I explained in the last section, the local time of a place depends on its longitude, and to start with, each town used its own local time. Only when the railways came, from the 1830's onward, was it necessary to have a uniform time throughout a country, so that timetables could be drawn up, for example.

The mean solar time at the Greenwich Observatory became the legal time throughout Britain from 1848, and other

PHOTO 5. b. John Harrison built his fourth chronometer in 1759. It was beautifully made and only 5 inches across. It won a prize of $48,000.00 when it lost only five seconds during a five-month voyage from Britain to Jamaica in the West Indies.

countries soon introduced similar laws. But there were still awkward time differences between countries; French time was 9 minutes 21 seconds ahead of Greenwich Mean Time, for example. Watches were even made with two sets of hands to show different times.

Only during this century have different countries agreed to divide the world up into time zones. Each of these time zones is a whole number of hours ahead of Greenwich Mean Time if to the east, or behind if to the west. On the other side of the world from Greenwich the zones 12 hours ahead and 12 hours behind Greenwich time meet, and the International Date Line is drawn between them, across the Pacific Ocean. Legally there is a difference of 24 hours (or one day) in the time on either side of this line. The line could have been drawn from north to south anywhere in the world, of course.

The crystal clock

Many things besides ordinary pendulums go through the rhythmical motion that can be used to control a clock. For example, crystals can be made to vibrate very rapidly. In the 1920's, scientists discovered that these vibrations are very regular. They used this discovery to build clocks controlled by crystals of quartz. These clocks can keep time ten times as accurately as the finest pendulum clocks.

Quartz crystal clocks are used in astronomical observatories and in other places where a very accurate time standard is needed. One common kind was designed by Dr. L. Essen at the National Physical Laboratory near London (Photo 6). It uses a crystal cut into a ring 2½ inches across. The vibration of the crystal sets up electrical vibrations within itself as well, and it is actually these vibrations which are used to control the clock. The crystal is hung from threads and electrodes attached to it to pick up the electrical vibrations. Electrical impulses are also used to keep the crystal vibrating.

The crystal has a frequency of vibration of 100,000 cycles (10 kilocycles) a second. Special electrical circuits, doing the same job as gears in mechanical clocks, are needed to reduce this frequency to something which can control the electric motor which drives the clock. There are many other complications, so that crystal clocks are expensive and bulky affairs. But they are so accurate that if one was left to run without being put right it would not be wrong by more than a second after 20 years.

Asking the atoms again

Seeking ever more accurate ways of measuring time, scientists eventually got down to using the vibrations of atoms. Various

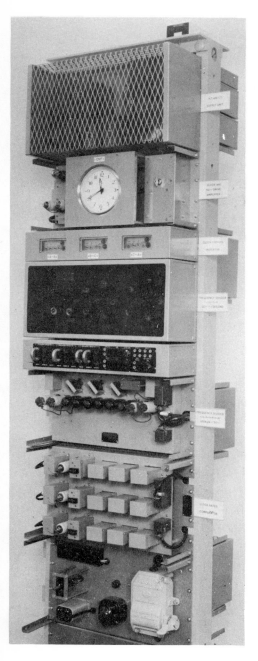

PHOTO 6. b. The quartz crystal itself is quite small. This one, from a clock used by the Greenwich Observatory, is in the shape of a ring about $2\frac{1}{2}$ inches across. Here it is shown in its holder with the cover removed.

PHOTO 6. a. Quartz crystal clocks like this one are bulky because of all the electrical equipment involved in them.

kinds of atomic clock have been made or suggested, but they all use the same idea. The secret is that the frequency of atomic vibrations is very sharply defined. In other words, if you have a lot of atoms of the same kind together they will all make very nearly the same number of vibrations in a second. This means that if the vibrations are used to control a clock, it will run more steadily and constantly than it could be made to in any other way.

The first atomic clock to be more accurate than crystal clocks was built in 1956. It used the vibrations of cesium atoms to regulate the speed of a quartz crystal clock, and one of its makers was the same Dr. Essen who designed the quartz crystal clock mentioned in the last section.

Cesium is a rare metal, and it was chosen because its atoms are magnetic in a rather convenient way. You can imagine each cesium atom as containing two tiny spinning magnets. They both wobble on their axes like spinning tops exactly 9,192,631,770 times a second. The total magnetism of the atom depends on whether the two little magnets are pointing in the same direction, or in exactly opposite directions, or somewhere in between.

In an atomic clock a stream of cesium atoms flows through a magnetic field which sorts them out into groups depending on how magnetic they are. Then one of the groups is passed through a field of radio waves. The vibrations of these radio waves are controlled by a quartz clock so as to have exactly the same frequency as the magnetic wobble of the cesium atoms. This means the radio waves *resonate* with the cesium atoms and make the little magnets flip over and change direction. Then another magnetic field sorts out the atoms which have changed their magnetism in this way and a special detector records them.

Now if the vibrations of the crystal in the quartz clock change at all, because of temperature changes for example, the frequency of the radio waves changes as well. The atomic magnets are no longer made to flip over and the detector notices this immediately. It sends out a warning and the clock is corrected automatically to allow for the change in the crystal. The cesium atoms are used to keep the quartz clock under strict control rather than as a clock in themselves.

A clock can be controlled so accurately in this way that it would be wrong by only a single second after running 3,000 years. Since atomic clocks keep time better than the Earth itself, they are used whenever the most accurate possible time is needed. Portable cesium clocks have been made so that time standards can be compared internationally as well. Scientists now believe that an atomic clock using hydrogen gas might be even more accurate than the cesium clock.

3 Nature's clocks

The daily rhythm

Nature has her own ways of measuring time. Animals and plants show the effects of time by growing weaker and less efficient with age. They also have their own built-in "clocks" to tell them what time of day or night it is, and for measuring short periods of time as well.

Naturalists have studied the internal clock by keeping animals in complete darkness for weeks or even months on end. They have found that, even with no day or night to divide up their lives, animals still keep to a regular timetable. They go through the cycle of waking and sleeping about every 24 hours just as they would in their normal lives. But often the length of the cycle is a few minutes longer or shorter than 24 hours.

Flying squirrels were used in one experiment. They usually sleep all day and are active only at night. When put in complete darkness the squirrels kept to this daily rhythm of sleep and activity — with one difference. Each evening they woke up a few minutes earlier, so that after a few weeks they were fully active while it was still broad daylight outside (Fig. 13).

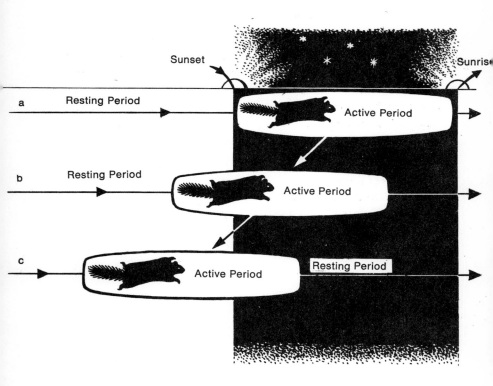

FIG. 13. a. Normally flying squirrels are active only at night.
b. If they are put in complete darkness, they have to rely on their internal clock to tell the time. This clock is often a little fast, so the squirrels wake up a few minutes earlier each evening.
c. After being kept in complete darkness for a week or so, they are active when it is broad daylight outside.

It was as if their clock ran a little fast, gaining a few minutes each day. This showed they must have been relying on their own internal clock. Had they some way, unknown to us, of telling whether it was night or day outside, they should not have got out of step with the real cycle of night and day.

The squirrels soon put their clock right when returned to ordinary daylight. So do all other animals and plants which scientists have found to have internal clocks, although they may be a little disturbed for a while, until they get used to the change. Even algae, which are very simple, single-celled water plants, can tell the time of day. If they are kept in the dark, even a short flash of light is enough to make them believe the day has begun and reset their clocks.

Living things need their clocks to time their activities and guide all the chemical rhythms going on inside them. They have other uses as well. Some birds use their internal clocks to help them find directions. If their clock tells them it is noon, then they know that south is in the direction of the Sun. Naturalists have proved this by using artificial light to make starlings set their clocks wrong. When they were put back into ordinary daylight the birds got their directions wrong as well. Probably migrating birds use this method to help their navigation.

Nature's clock is used to keep track of the seasons of the year as well. Tobacco plants, for example, get the signal to flower from the lengthening of the days in springtime. They can be persuaded to flower in other seasons by changing the length of the day with artificial light. Their clocks must keep time to within two minutes a day to detect the season so accurately.

Some birds also seem to learn when to breed or migrate

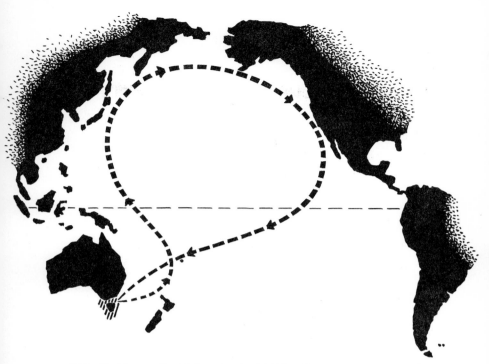

FIG. 14. The muttonbirds migrate 21,000 miles every year, traveling right around the Pacific Ocean, but they always arrive back in Tasmania on the same days.

from the changing length of the day. At least one kind, the muttonbird, which lives on the island of Tasmania, south of Australia, seems to have a very accurate internal calendar. Each year the muttonbird migrates north by way of Japan to Alaska, and then returns down the west coast of the Americas to complete a 21,000-mile circuit of the Pacific Ocean (Fig. 14). The astonishing thing is that the first returning birds always arrive back in Tasmania on the night of September 26, and have done so ever since records were first kept in the 1860's. Scientists do not believe that the muttonbird does this by noticing the changing length of the day, because it changes a lot on a long journey from north to south in any case. On the other hand, nobody has any other explanation for such perfect timekeeping.

Pacemaker in the brain

On July 16, 1962, Michel Siffre, a French geologist, clambered down into a cave in the Alps. He had with him all the food and equipment needed for a two-month stay underground — except a watch. His only link with the outside world was by telephone. He used it to tell helpers on the surface when he ate or slept and they kept a record of his timetable. Siffre noted down his own estimates of these times as well.

Siffre's time calculations turned out to be completely wrong compared to those of his helpers on the surface. He divided his daily cycle of rising, working, eating and sleeping into a shorter than normal cycle he thought to be 15 hours long. When he figured he had been in the cave 36 days (by adding up the 15 hour cycles), he came to the surface. He was surprised to find that he had actually spent 61 days in the cave. What he thought to be 15 hour cycles were actually 24½ hour cycles.

Michel Siffre's experiment showed two things about the way people's internal clocks work. First he demonstrated that, like so many animals and plants, we do have some sort of built-in 24-hour rhythm, even if we do not realize it; secondly, that time spent in a dull, boring way actually passes more quickly than we realize. Both those discoveries have been confirmed by many less daring experiments. The second is equally true of the way we estimate much shorter lengths of time.

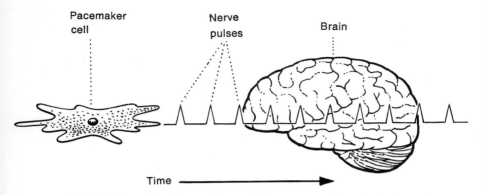

FIG. 15. According to one theory of the way our internal clock works, we have "pacemaker cells" which send out regular nerve pulses. These are unconsciously counted by the brain, and the number it counts tells us how long a time has passed.

They were surprising discoveries. Most people certainly believe that dull or boring work makes time pass slowly. Why do people doing such jobs actually think less time has passed than really has? It can be explained by looking at one possible theory of the way our internal clocks work.

According to this theory we all have built-in *pacemakers.* These pacemakers may be a particular sort of nerve cell — we are not sure — but whatever they are, they send out pulses at regular intervals, perhaps every tenth of a second (Fig. 15). These pulses pass along a nerve one after the other, like cars in a freight train. A counter adds up how many have passed along the nerve in a particular length of time, and a memory keeps a record of the number. If a person needs to estimate a length of time, his brain unconsciously counts the number of pulses sent out by the pacemaker during that time. Then the count is compared with the stored records for other lengths of time to find out how much has passed.

According to this theory, if we are bored, or not exerting ourselves very much, the nerve cells slow down and send out pulses at longer intervals. In other words, our own internal clock starts to run slow. Instead of ten pulses passing along the nerve in a second it may take one and a half seconds for the counter to reach ten. All our estimates of time are thrown out as a result. We think only one second has passed when in fact one and a half seconds have gone by; or, like Michel Siffre, we think we have been in the cave for only 36 days when really we have spent 61 days underground.

This means that human beings, and, to judge from other experiments, animals too, have two internal clocks. One works quite unconsciously and keeps us to a 24-hour cycle. The other is what we use for deliberately estimating time, and is much more easily influenced by outside events. Besides going slowly if we are bored, it seems to run faster if we are ill with a temperature, for example. But so far scientists have no clear idea how either of these clocks works.

Altering the clock

What happens to people whose internal clock is reset? This is becoming an important problem nowadays. Modern industry needs more and more people to work on shifts, who must be wide awake and efficient in the middle of the night. Then the next week they may have to work at the normal time again. Jet planes now fly so fast that they almost keep up with the turning of the Earth. They cross the Atlantic in seven hours, but the time in New York is five hours behind London. An air traveler who leaves London at 8 A.M. finds it is still only 10 A.M. when he gets to New York. Somehow his internal clock has to adjust to a day with five extra hours in it.

Jet travelers find they take up to five days to get used to the time change after a long flight. In the meantime they are tired, their sense of time is confused, and they are less efficient than usual. Many of the body's processes keep to a daily rhythm, heartbeat, blood pressure, breathing and temperature among them. They are all working hardest during our waking hours, so that we are at our best then. If we go on a long journey, with a big time change, or abruptly start working in the middle of the night and sleeping during daylight, most of the processes adapt quite quickly to the new rhythm. But some may take months to adjust and there is no way for our minds to control them.

Experiments in the Arctic show that the human body adapts more quickly than usual to shift work there during the winter, when there is no light to confuse the internal clock. When people are blinded — in an accident for example — their internal clock often starts to go wrong as well. Apparently our clock is set by daylight, just as it is in primitive animals and plants.

When supersonic passenger jets start operating in the 1970's the problem of the time change will be even greater. The Concord supersonic airliner will fly faster than the Sun moves across the sky. At 1,400 miles an hour it will cross the Atlantic in three hours. If a Concord leaves London at 8 A.M., the time will still be only 6 A.M. when it arrives in New York (Fig. 16). It will be quite easy to fly from London to New York in the morning, then leave New York again in the afternoon and be back in London by midnight. What will happen to the traveler's internal clock? Will it become hopelessly confused; or will it just not notice that it has been through two time changes in one day?

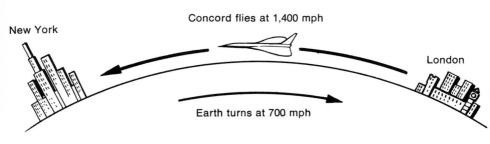

New York

Concord flies at 1,400 mph

London

Earth turns at 700 mph

FIG. 16. The Concord supersonic airliner will fly faster than the Earth turns. This means that when it crosses the Atlantic, it will arrive two hours earlier in the day than when it left London.

Time and aging

Everyone can see some of the ways the passing of time affects people. Hair changes its color, skin wrinkles and loses its springiness, the body grows weaker, and sight, hearing or taste become less sensitive. Hidden changes take place inside the body as well. The result of it all is that as we grow old we are less able to resist diseases or accidents, and so more likely to die.

About the age of seventy the likelihood of death begins to increase sharply. Old age comes just as soon as it did in Old Testament days, when "three score years and ten" was considered the span of a man's natural life. Modern medical science has made sure that more of us live to see old age — but it has not slowed down the process of aging itself (Fig. 17).

On the average, boy babies born in America today can expect to live for 68 years. For some reason women tend to live longer than men, so girl babies can expect to live 74 years on the average. A century ago the average life-span in America was much shorter — only 40 years — and in ancient Greece and Rome it was probably about 30 years. This was largely because in those days many babies died in the first few years of their lives, which brought the average life-span down a lot. Even today, 25 out of every 1,000 babies born in America die before they are one year old.

FIG. 17. This diagram shows what ages people die at in the United States. You can see that more people die between seventy and eighty than at any other age.

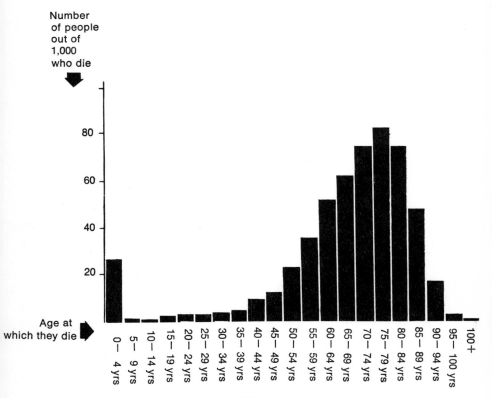

Man seems to be the longest-lived of the mammals (animals which feed milk to their young). Pierre Joubert, a French Canadian from Quebec, lived 113 years 100 days and died in 1814. No one has ever been proved to have lived longer than this, although there have been several who claimed to be over 150 years old. Indian elephants are probably the next most long-lived mammals. They sometimes reach the age of eighty. The oldest horses live to nearly forty, cats to about twenty-five, and dogs to about twenty years; but these are equivalent to human centenarians.

Birds and fish live surprisingly long when given the chance, although birds particularly have such dangerous lives that they rarely survive to old age. Vultures, eagles and parrots have been said to reach 100. Some sturgeon, the fish from which caviar comes, live at least 75 years and maybe much more. Their age can be found by cutting across the back fin, which shows yearly rings of growth rather like a tree.

But the animals which live longest of all, as far as we know, are tortoises. One which lived on the island of Tonga in the South Pacific, until it died in 1966, was supposed to have been given to the king of the island by Captain Cook, the explorer. Cook visited Tonga for the last time in 1777, so if the story is true the tortoise must have been at least 189 years old when it died. Another tortoise died at the age of 116 at Paignton Zoo in Devonshire.

The many scientists who have studied aging have not been able to discover much about why it takes place. One theory is that aging happens because cells which cannot be replaced get damaged or worn out and eventually die. In some parts of the body, cells are always dividing and producing new cells to replace any which die or get worn away. In others, such as the liver and the kidneys, new cells can be produced if needed.

But muscle and nerve cells do not divide at all once an animal is fully grown. If one of these cells is lost it cannot be replaced. As animals get older, the theory says, nerve and muscle cells get clogged up with waste materials, and slow chemical changes eventually stop them from working properly. In the end they die, so the animal loses its strength and its brain and nervous system become less efficient.

This theory fits in well with a lot of the facts we know about aging, but there seem to be other things happening as well. The "cement" that bonds our cells, called *collagen,* goes through chemical changes as it grows older and loses some of its firmness and springiness. This is why people's skins wrinkle with age. No one knows yet how important the wearing out of collagen is in the aging process. Scientists have also shown that extra doses of atomic radiation make animals age faster. Is the background atomic radiation which is always reaching the Earth from space partly responsible for aging as well? No one knows yet. Experiments are going on all over the world to find out, but it may be many years before scientists can say just why we grow older.

4 Less than a second

Recorded time

Speed cannot be separated from time. We could just as well say of Dr. Roger Bannister, the first man (in 1954) to run a mile in under four minutes, that he was the first to average more than 15 miles an hour for a mile. Speed is simply the distance covered by something in a certain time, whether it is a snail, a jet plane or a wave of light. Very often both scientists and sportsmen measure time in order to work out speed.

If they are not too short, these lengths of time can be measured by the same kinds of clock that we use in ordinary life. Stopwatches are driven by the same mechanisms as wristwatches. The only difference is that they are fitted with a device to start the hands moving, stop them at the end of the race (or whatever it is), and return them to zero. Nowadays some wristwatches are fitted with controls so that they too can be used as stopwatches.

Besides timing sporting events, stopwatches are needed in many scientific experiments and in industry. Time-and-motion study depends on measuring the minutes and seconds needed for the different actions involved in doing a job of work. For example, suppose the job was washing up the dishes after dinner. The time-study man would find out how long it took to clear the table, run the water, wash the dishes, rinse them and dry them. He would try to break up all these actions into their individual parts, and then he might be able to suggest a quicker or easier way of doing it. By examining factory jobs in this way, he can often help to make them much more efficient; but the task would be impossible without an accurate way of measuring time.

The first stopwatches were made in the eighteenth century. They were not very accurate because the means of stopping and starting the mechanism was too clumsy. Ordinary modern stopwatches are accurate to one-fifth of a second. It is useless to make them much better than this because people's reactions are not fast enough to measure time to less than one-tenth of a second.

Electrically controlled stopwatches can respond much more quickly, and nowadays they are used for timing important races. The stopwatch is told of the start and finish of the race by an electric signal so it can be accurate to a hundredth of a second or even less. There are *photo-finish* cameras which actually show the winner's time in the picture (Photo 7). The first electrically operated stopwatch, called a *chronoscope,* was made in 1840 by Sir Charles Wheatstone, who had many electrical inventions to his credit. He used it for measuring the speed of a bullet from a pistol. Modern chronoscopes are

PHOTO 7. Electronic stopwatches can now be combined with photo-finish cameras to show the winner's time in a race underneath the picture. The numbers at the bottom of the picture show times in seconds and tenths of a second.

controlled by the vibrations of an electric tuning fork, which takes the part of a pendulum or a quartz crystal. Although they are accurate to one ten-thousandth of a second they are not used much nowadays. A different sort of electrical time-keeper, called an *oscilloscope*, is much more convenient.

The *chronograph* is another kind of timekeeper with many uses. You may have come across weather recorders, for example; they can sometimes be seen at work in museums, or even in the shop windows of opticians. They record the changes in temperature and air pressure throughout the 24 hours.

PHOTO 8. Recording chronographs are essential in factories to keep track of quantities which change with time. This one is being used to record the temperature of steam.

Often they have two pens, one connected to a thermometer, the other to a barometer (for measuring air pressure). Then there is a drum turned by clockwork, which usually takes a week to complete one revolution.

Each week a piece of paper is fitted on the drum, having the hours marked on it one way and temperature and air pressure the other. As the drum turns, the pens trace the changing temperature and air pressure across it, to make a continuous record of the weather. If you look at one of the records you can see how the temperature rises in the morning and early afternoon and drops back in the evening. Often you can see just when a particular weather event occurred, such as a rainstorm or a sunny interval.

Recording chronographs are essential in industry. Modern chemical factories, for example, could not work without having them to keep track of changes during the day (Photo 8). Usually a changing temperature, pressure, strength, or whatever it is, is translated into electrical oscillations. These oscillations are made to power an electromagnet, which influences a magnetic pen to trace a line on a moving drum or strip of paper. Automation, which makes it possible for factories, such as steel mills and oil refineries, to run themselves, with only a few men watching over them, depends a lot on this sort of equipment.

Water clocks brought up to date

The old idea of the water clock is being used for measuring time more than ever today, but in a modern form. Nowadays electricity takes the place of water, and the measuring device is called an *electronic time base.* Instead of a water container slowly emptying or filling, it employs something called a *capacitance,* which is really just a reservoir for electricity. And it measures not hours but thousandths of a second.

Electronic time bases are used in the instruments noted earlier, called oscilloscopes, which are closely related to ordinary television sets. Oscilloscopes are used to make electric currents visible. Scientists often translate effects they want to watch or measure into electric signals. Whatever it is they are studying — an animal's heartbeats, for example, or the vibrations of a machine — can usually be put into the form of an electric current. Then this current can be fed into an oscilloscope. Instead of drawing out the pattern of the current with a pen on paper, the instrument traces it out as a line of light on the screen, in much the same way as a television set traces out a picture.

Suppose an engineer wants to study the vibrations in a piece of machinery. They will produce a wave-shaped electric current which repeats itself perhaps a hundred times a second, depending on how rapid the vibrations are. In this case, the engineer would say they had a frequency of 100 cycles a second. But if he were to try to watch a hundred waves passing across the oscilloscope screen every second, he would learn very little.

This is where the time base comes in. The engineer so adjusts it that it makes the point of light tracing out the pattern

FIG. 18. An oscilloscope makes electric waves show up as a line of light on a screen. The user can measure the distance between the waves using the grid on the screen, and this tells him the time interval between the waves.

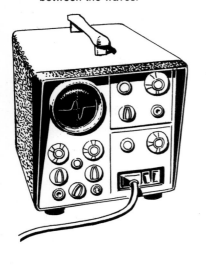

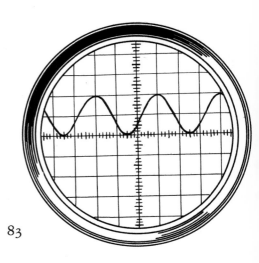

cross the screen in a hundredth of a second, and then return to its starting place. The result is that the waves are repeated again and again in exactly the same position, on top of each other; in short, they are "frozen" (Fig. 18). What he sees is a single stationary wave. Time is translated into lengths this way because the width of the screen is arranged to represent one hundredth of a second, half the width representing half that time, and so on. This means the engineer can see what shape the vibration has, and measure parts of it to find out how long it takes.

Of course, the frequency of the vibration is not often exactly one hundred cycles a second. With ordinary instruments it is possible to measure waves with frequencies as high as 20,000 cycles a second. Special instruments, called *synchroscopes,* mark off intervals of a millionth of a second with a point of light on the screen. They can be used to measure time intervals as short as two-billionths of a second (or 2 *nanoseconds*).

Oscilloscopes are used for a tremendous variety of jobs — they are probably the scientist's most important instrument — but it is time measurement that we are concerned with in this book. The time base is the clock in an oscilloscope. As I said before, it works rather like a water clock. The capacitance is charged, or filled up with electricity, until it reaches a certain voltage. Then it abruptly empties or discharges through an electronic circuit. The voltage falls back to zero, and the whole process begins again.

The length of time the cycle of charge and discharge takes fixes the length of the time base. The difference is that the time a capacitance takes to fill with electricity is much more constant than the time it takes to fill a bucket, so an electronic time base is much more accurate than a water clock. What is more, the length of an oscilloscope's time base is altered simply by turning a knob to change the capacitance.

You don't meet oscilloscopes much in ordinary life but very few scientific laboratories are without them these days. It is not only people working on electronics or engineering who use them. Biologists, for example, need them to follow the tiny electric currents that are always passing through our brains and along our nerves. In one experiment an oscilloscope is connected to two points on the nerve running down a frog's leg. Then nerve pulses can be seen on the instrument's screen as they travel to and from the leg muscle. By measuring the time it takes for the pulse to travel from one electrical contact to the next the scientist can find out its speed — usually about 120 feet a second.

Time and Dr. Einstein

The connection between speed and time is usually a simple one, but when the speeds get very high indeed it becomes much more complicated. This is one of the conclusions of the famous *theory of relativity*, proposed by Albert Einstein, the great mathematician and physicist. The simple part of his theory, called the "special theory," is not nearly so hard to understand as is often supposed. It has some important things to say about the nature of time, and the way we experience it.

In 1887 two American scientists called Michelson and Morley carried out a very careful experiment to measure the speed of light. They proved that its speed when traveling through empty space is always the same — 186,000 miles a second — no matter how fast the source of light itself is traveling. (Other electromagnetic waves, such as radio signals and X rays, travel at the same speed. They are just the same as light waves except that they have different frequencies — and, of course, we cannot see them.)

To show what this means, suppose you have a spaceship traveling past a space station at 10,000 miles an hour. Suppose then there is a light on the spaceship and another on the station, both shining in the direction the spaceship is traveling. You would expect that the light waves from the ship would travel 10,000 miles an hour faster than the light from the station. But this is not so. The light from both travels at exactly the same speed, no matter how fast the spaceship goes.

This fact bothered scientists a lot after Michelson and Morley's experiment, until Einstein came along and based his theory of relativity upon it. Some of the consequences are surprising. Seen from the space station, the spaceship will seem to be shorter than it was before it started moving. Clocks on board the spaceship will run more slowly than on the station, and that applies to biological clocks as well. Time will pass more slowly on the spaceship. It is rather as if the speed of light is a barrier, and time and distance get squashed up as they are pressed against it.

How big these effects are depends on how fast the spaceship is moving compared with the speed of light. Ten thousand miles an hour, or three miles a second, is nothing compared with the 186,000 miles a second at which light travels, so relativity would make very little difference to a spaceship traveling at that speed. But if it could travel much faster the slowing down of time on board the spaceship would get greater and greater as its speed got closer to the speed of light.

If it could travel as fast as light, time would be slowed down to nothing; but Einstein's theory also shows this to be impossible.

Think what this strange time effect would mean to men on a spaceship traveling away from our Sun to the stars, which are bodies just like our Sun, but very far away. Light from the nearest, called Alpha Centauri, takes nearly $4\frac{1}{2}$ years to reach us. Suppose we could build a spaceship that could travel at nine-tenths of the speed of light. Measured by clocks on Earth, it would take ten years to get to Alpha Centauri and come straight back. But for the men on the ship, time would be slowed down and the journey would take only four years and four months. When they got back they would be more than five years younger than people born at the same time who had stayed behind!

Although nobody has been able to undertake such a journey, of course, there is proof that this slowing down of time really does happen. It concerns tiny atomic particles called *pi-mesons,* which can be made artificially on Earth by firing atoms at each other at tremendous speeds in particle accelerators (atom smashers). Pi-mesons live for only a hundred-millionth of a second (10 nanoseconds) before breaking up into other kinds of particles.

They are also made when cosmic rays from space, themselves composed of very fast-moving atomic particles, collide with the atoms of the air in the Earth's upper atmosphere (Fig. 19). Some of the pi-mesons created in this way can be detected at ground level. Even at the speed of light it must take them a ten-thousandth of a second to reach the ground from the upper atmosphere. In other words, they have lived

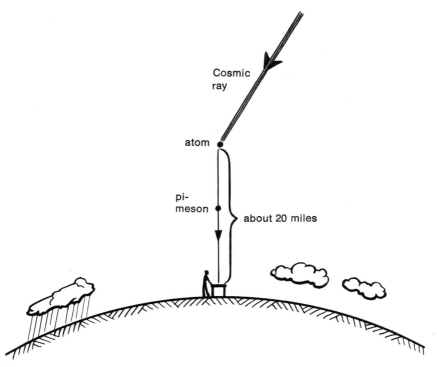

FIG. 19. Pi-mesons created when cosmic rays from space collide with atoms in the upper atmosphere provide a proof of Einstein's theory of relativity. Traveling at almost the speed of light, they take only one ten-thousandths of a second to cover the 20 miles to the ground, but this is ten thousand times as long as they normally live.

ten thousand times as long as they normally do because, when traveling very close to the speed of light, time passes ten thousand times as slowly for them.

Einstein's theory means that time is not the same all over the universe. Instead it is a local thing. Each spot in the universe has its own time, depending on how it is moving in relation to other parts of the universe (that is why it is called the theory of *relativity*). The theory upset the old idea of time, but scientists are still not sure what they should put in its place.

In 1964 another experiment with atomic particles seemed to upset another old idea about time. This was that the flow of time could be reversed without making any difference to scientific laws and the way things behave. Physicists now believe this to be untrue, but they are not sure just what their discovery does mean. It is going to be very exciting to see what they learn about time in the years to come.

The shortest times

This book began by asking, "What are the oldest things of all?" It is ending by asking what are the shortest lengths of time scientists have been able to measure. The answer is: roughly a thousandth of a millionth of a millionth of a second. And just as the book began by talking about the ways radioisotopes are used to measure the age of the Earth and so on, it ends by talking about radioisotopes once more: how, in fact, scientists measure the half-lives of the very short-lived ones.

You may remember that radioisotopes are atoms which are unstable so that eventually they break up, giving off radioactivity. The half-life of a radioisotope is the time it takes for half the atoms of the isotope to decay in this way. Some half-lives are many millions of years long; others are tiny fractions of a second. It is the latter which interest us now.

Down to about a billionth of a second, or one nanosecond, physicists can measure half-lives using electronic equipment such as oscilloscopes and similar apparatus. One simple way is to create a quantity of the radioisotope being studied in an atomic accelerator, then watch with special detectors for the burst of radiation as the new isotope quickly decays. The half-life is found by measuring the time it takes for the new radiation to die away.

Direct measurements of times less than a nanosecond are difficult. The speed with which electronic devices such as transistors can respond to electric currents decides how short is the length of time they can measure. Even the time it takes for the current to travel along the wires of an electronic measuring circuit begins to cause difficulties where time intervals of a nanosecond are involved. At 186,000 miles a second, electricity can travel only about a foot of wire in a nanosecond. Engineers must face all these problems when they build high-speed computers. Nowadays some of the biggest and most powerful of these electronic calculating machines carry out simple operations in 200 to 300 nanoseconds, and they are getting faster all the time.

So if a physicist wants to measure half-lives of much less than a nanosecond he has to find ingenious ways of doing it. It is not possible to make a clock which will measure such short times directly. But one of the best ways of solving the problem is also surprisingly simple.

The first step is to make some of the radioisotope by bom-

FIG. 20. These three drawings illustrate one way of measuring the half-lives of very short-lived radioisotopes.
a. Atomic bullets are shot at a target from an accelerator.
b. The bullets change atoms in the target into radioactive atoms which bounce back.
c. After traveling a very short distance, the new atoms decay, giving off gamma rays. A detector picks up the gamma rays to see how far the radioactive atoms did travel before decaying. From knowing how fast the atoms were traveling as well, it is easy to work out how long they took to decay, and so their half-life can be found.

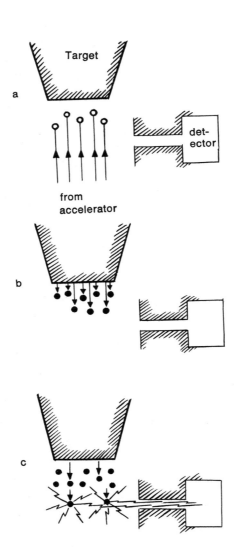

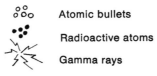

Atomic bullets

Radioactive atoms

Gamma rays

barding a target with fast-moving atoms from an accelerator. The atoms of the new radioisotope bounce back but they do not travel very far before decaying because their half-life is so short. The scientist can work out how fast they must be traveling from knowing how energetic the atoms from the accelerator were. He can see how far the new atoms travel, by detecting the radiation they give off when they decay, called gamma rays (Fig. 20). From there it is easy to work out how long, on the average, they take to decay, and from this how long their half-life is.

By methods like this physicists have been able to measure half-lives as short as 0.000 000 000 000 001 seconds. This is roughly the half-life of the isotope beryllium-8. When it gets down to times as short as this, measurement is not very accurate, and the actual half-life may be four times longer or shorter than this.

No doubt scientists will learn to measure even shorter times before long, and more accurately too. Perhaps also they will be able to go even further back into the past than the six or seven billion years that is believed to be the age of the atoms. But already they have done well in measuring time. The longest time that has been measured is about a thousand million million million million million (1,000,000,000,000, 000,000,000,000,000,000,000) times as long as the shortest one.

Atomic clocks measure time more accurately than any other physical quantity can be measured. But even though we can measure it so exactly time remains a mysterious thing — far more puzzling and intangible than length or mass, or even temperature, for example.

Index

About the Author

TIMOTHY JOHNSON is a young Englishman whose travels have brought him to Europe, the Near East, and the United States. He was educated in England where he received his B.S. degree in physics at Imperial College in London. RIVER OF TIME is Mr. Johnson's first book, but his literary career began in 1962 as a scientific journalist for the *Statist*. Upon receiving his degree in 1963, he became the assistant science correspondent of the *Daily Telegraph* in London. Today he is the science editor of the *Illustrated London News* and the author of articles published in numerous scientific magazines and journals.